SO-AXD-060

Dear Parents,

Welcome to the Scholastic Reader series. We have taken over 80 years of experience with teachers, parents, and children and put it into a program that is designed to match your child's interests and skills.

Level 1—Short sentences and stories made up of words kids can sound out using their phonics skills and words that are important to remember.

Level 2—Longer sentences and stories with words kids need to know and new "big" words that they will want to know.

Level 3—From sentences to paragraphs to longer stories, these books have large "chunks" of texts and are made up of a rich vocabulary.

Level 4—First chapter books with more words and fewer pictures.

It is important that children learn to read well enough to succeed in school and beyond. Here are ideas for reading this book with your child:

- Look at the book together. Encourage your child to read the title and make a prediction about the story.
- Read the book together. Encourage your child to sound out words when appropriate. When your child struggles, you can help by providing the word.
- Encourage your child to retell the story. This is a great way to check for comprehension.
- Have your child take the fluency test on the last page to check progress.

Scholastic Readers are designed to support your child's efforts to learn how to read at every age and every stage. Enjoy helping your child learn to read and love to read.

— **Francie Alexander**
Chief Education Officer
Scholastic Education

For Jonathan—the Brat

Copyright © 1995 by Nancy Hall, Inc.
Fluency activities copyright © 2003 Scholastic Inc.
All rights reserved. Published by Scholastic Inc.
SCHOLASTIC, CARTWHEEL BOOKS, and associated logos
are trademarks and/or registered trademarks of Scholastic Inc.

Library of Congress Cataloging-in-Publication Data is available.

ISBN: 0-439-62596-3

10 9 8 7 6 5 4 3 2   06 07
Printed in the U.S.A. 23 • First printing, February 1995

My Brother, the Brat

by **Kirsten Hall**

Illustrated by **Joan Holub**

Scholastic Reader — Level 1

SCHOLASTIC INC. Cartwheel ·B·O·O·K·S·®

New York   Toronto   London   Auckland   Sydney
Mexico City   New Delhi   Hong Kong   Buenos Aires

See my brother.

What a brat.

See him take my baseball bat!

See him take my choo-choo train.

See my brother.
What a pain!

I will take his
teddy bear.

I can take it?
You don't care?

I can take your fire truck?

Then you can take my rubber duck.

You can take it! I don't care!

Little brother, we can share.

Your Favorite Toy

What is your favorite toy?
Why is it your favorite toy?
How did you get this toy?
Did you pick it out?
Was it a present?

Rhyme Time

Rhyming words sound alike. For each word on the left, point to the word on the right that rhymes with it.

pain	my
duck	bat
I	truck
brat	train

Sports Fun

Point to the things that you would use for playing sports.

Now, point to the things that you would not use for playing sports.

Many Ways to Say It

Sometimes, a sentence has more than one meaning depending on how you say it. By changing your tone of voice or the look on your face, you can make a sentence mean different things.

Look at this sentence.

Little brother, we can share.

Say it out loud in a way that sounds friendly.

Say it out loud in a way that sounds like a question.

Now say the sentence another way.

Where's the B?

Some of these words start with the letter **b**. Some start with another letter. Point to the words that start with **b**.

baseball	brat
brother	pain
duck	bear
bat	truck

Clowning Around

Find the clown:

He is not wearing stripes.

He has purple shoes.

He is not wearing a hat.

He is not smiling.

Which one is he?

Answers

(*Your Favorite Toy*)
Answers will vary.

(*Rhyme Time*)

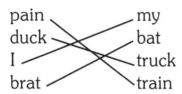

pain — train
duck — truck
I — my
brat — bat

(*Sports Fun*)
You would use:

You would not use:

(*Many Ways to Say It*)
Answers will vary.

(*Where's the B?*)

baseball   **brat**
brother   **bear**
bat

(*Clowning Around*)
This is the clown: